The Essential Aussie Songbook

Exclusive Distributors for the Music Trade: **Music Sales Pty. Limited**
120 Rothschild Avenue, Rosebery, NSW 2018, Australia.

Exclusive Distributors for Recorded Music Retailers: **MRA**
5 Dividend St, Mansfield QLD 4122, Australia.

This book © Copyright 2000 by Wise Publications
Order No: MS03718
Book Only ISBN: 0949789836
Book & Double CD ISBN: 0949789933

Reprinted 2002

Cover Design by Ken Done.
Printed in Australia by McPhersons Printing Group.

Music Sales Pty. Limited.
Lisgar House,
Level 4 / 32 Carrington St., Sydney, NSW 2000, Australia.

Wise Publications
London/New York/Sydney/Paris/Copenhagen/Madrid

The Essential Aussie Songbook Contents

1
A Pub With No Beer

Gordon Parsons

1. It's lone - some a - way from your kin - dred and all, By the camp - fire at night where the wild din - goes call; But there's noth - ing so lone - some, So mor - bid or drear, Than to stand in a bar of a pub with no beer.

Now the beer.

2. Now the publican's anxious
   For the quota to come,
   There's a far away look
   On the face of the "bum";
   The maid's gone all cranky,
   And cook's acting queer,
   What a terrible place
   Is a pub with no beer.

3. Then the stockman rides up
   With his dry dusty throat,
   He breasts up to the bar,
   Pulls a wad from his coat,
   But the smile on his face
   Quickly turns to a sneer,
   When the barman says sadly:
   "The pub's got not beer."

4. Then the swaggie comes in
   Smothered in dust and flies,
   He throws down his roll,
   Rubs the sweat from his eyes;
   But when he is told he says:
   "What's this I hear?
   Spoken: I've trudged fifty flamin' miles
   To a pub with no beer."

SUNG: 5. There's a dog on the v'randah,
   For his master he waits,
   But the boss is inside
   Drinking wine with his mates;
   He hurries for cover
   And he cringes in fear,
   It's no place for a dog
   'Round a pub with no beer.

6. Old Billy the Blacksmith,
   The first time in his life
   Has gone home cold sober
   To his darling wife;
   He walks in the kitchen,
   She says: "You're early my dear,"
   But he breaks down and tells her:
   "The pub's got no beer."

7. It's lonesome away
   From your kindred and all,
   By the campfire at night
   Where the wild dingoes call;
   But there's nothing so lonesome,
   So morbid or drear
   Than to stand in a bar
   Of a pub with no beer.

2
Advance Australia Fair

P. D. McCormick

1. Aus - tra - lians all let us re - joice, for we are young and free, We've gold - en soil and wealth for toil, Our home is girt by sea; Our land a - bounds in na - tures gifts of beau - ty rich and rare: In his - 'trys page let ev - 'ry stage ad - vance Aus - tra - lia fair, In joy - ful strains than let us sing ad - vance Aus - tra - lia fair.

2. Beneath our radiant Southern Cross
   We'll toil with hearts and hands,
   To make this Commonwealth of ours
   Renowned of all the lands,
   For those who've come across the seas
   We've boundless plains to share,
   With courage let us all combine
   To advance Australia fair.
   In joyful strains then let us sing,
   Advance Australia fair.

3
Along The Road To Gundagai

Jack O'Hagan

There's a scene that lingers in my memory,
Of an old bush home and friends I long to see.
That's why I am yearning, just to be returning
Along the road to Gundagai.

Chorus:
There's a track winding back to an old fashioned shack
Along the road to Gundagai:
Where the blue gums are growing and the Murrumbidgee's flowing,
Beneath that sunny sky;
Where my daddy and mother are waiting for me,
And the pals of my childhood once more I will see.
Then no more will I roam, when I'm heading right for home
Along the road to Gundagai.

When I get back there I'll be a kid again.
Oh! I'll never have a thought of grief or pain.
Once more I'll be playing, where the gums are swaying
Along the road to Gundagai.

4
And The Band Played Waltzing Matilda

Eric Bogle

V2. How well I remember that terrible day,
How the blood stained the sand and the water,
And how in that hell that they called Suvla Bay
We were butchered like lambs to the slaughter;
Johnny Turk he was waiting, he'd primed himself well,
He rained us with bullets and showered us with shells,
And in ten minutes flat he'd blown us all to hell,
Nearly blew us right back to Australia.

CHORUS:
But the band played "Waltzing Matilda",
When we stopped to bury the slain,
We buried ours, and the Turks buried theirs,
Then we started all over again.

V3. And those that were left, well, we tried to survive
In that mad world of death, blood and fire,
And for nearly ten weeks I kept myself alive,
Though around me the corpses piled higher;
Then a big Turkish shell knocked me arse over head,
And when I woke up in my hospital bed
I saw what it had done, and I wished I was dead,
Never knew there were worse things than dying.

CHORUS:
For I'll go no more waltzing Matilda
All around the wild bush far and free,
To hump tent and pegs, a man needs both legs,
No more waltzing Matilda for me.

V4. Then they gathered the sick and the crippled and maimed,
And sent us back home to Australia,
The armless, the legless, the blind and insane,
The brave wounded heroes of Suvla;
And when our ship pulled in to Circular Quay,
I looked at the stumps where my legs used to be,
And thanked Christ there was nobody waiting for me
To grieve, to mourn and to pity.

CHORUS:
And the band played "Waltzing Matilda"
As they carried us down the gangway,
But nobody cheered, they just stood there and stared,
Then they turned their faces away.

V5. So every April my old comrades march,
Reviving old dreams and past glory,
And I push my wheelchair out onto the porch,
And watch the parade pass before me;
The old men march slowly, old bones stiff and sore,
Tired old men from a forgotten war,
The young people ask: "What are they marching for?"
I ask myself the same question.

CHORUS:
And the band plays "Waltzing Matilda",
The old men respond to the call,
But as year follows year, more old men disappear,
Someday no - one will march there at all.

5
Black Velvet Band

Traditional

In a neat lit-tle town they call Bel-fast, _____ App-rent-iced to trade I was bound, _____ And

man-y an hour's sweet happ-i-ness, That I spent in that neat lit-tle town, _____ Till

sad mis-for-tune came o'er me, _____ And I had to flee from the land, _____ A-

way from my friends and re-la-tions, To fol-low the black vel-vet band. _____

Chorus: (To the air of the 2nd half of verse)
Her eyes they shone like the diamonds,
You'd think she was Queen of the land,
And her hair hung over her shoulder,
Tied up with a black velvet band.

As I went strolling one evening,
Not meaning to go very far,
I spied the pretty young damsel,
Parading her wares in the bar,
A watch she took from a customer,
And slipped it right into my hand,
And the law came and put me in prison,
:Bad luck to her black velvet band.

Next morning before judge and jury
For trial I had to appear,
And the judge said 'Me fine young fellow
The case against you is quite clear,
For seven long years is your sentence,
You're going to Van Diemen's Land,
Away from your friends and relations,
To follow the black velvet band'.

Now come all you jolly young fellows,
And a warning take from me,
And whenever you go out for liquor, lads,
Beware of the pretty colleen,
She'll fill you with whisky and porter,
Until you're unable to stand,
And the very next thing that you know me lads,
You've landed in Van Diemen's Land.

6
Botany Bay

Traditional

Fare - well to old Eng land for e - ver,_____ Fare - well to my rum culls as well;_____ Fare -

Repeat for Chorus

well to the well - known Old Bai - lee,_____ Where I used for to cut such a swell_____

Farewell to old England for ever,
Farewell to my rum culls as well;
Farewell to the well - known Old Bailee,
Where I used for to cut such a swell.

Chorus:
Singing too - ral li - ooral li - ad - dity
Singing too - ral li - ooral li - ay;
Singing too - ral li - ooral li - ad - dity
And we're bound for Botany Bay.

There's the Captain as is our Commander,
There's the bo'sun and all the ship's crew,
There's the first and second - class passengers,
Knows what we poor convicts go through.

'Taint leavin' old England we cares about,
'Taint cos we mispels what we knows,
But becos all we light - fingered gentry
Hops around with a log on our toes.

For seven long years I'll be staying here,
For seven long years and a day,
For meeting a cove in an area
And taking his ticker away.

Oh, had I the wings of a turtle - dove!
I'd soar on my pinions so high,
Slap bang to the arms of my Polly love,
And in her sweet presence I'd die.

Now, all my young Dookies and Duchesses,
Take warining from what I've to say,
Mind all is your own as you touchesses,
Or you'll find us in Botany Bay.

7
Bound For South Australia

Traditional

Oh, South Aus-tra-lia's my na-tive home. Heave a-way! Heave a-way! Oh,

south Aus-tra-lia's my na-tive home. We're bound for South Aus-tra-lia. Heave a-way,

heave a-way, Oh, heave a-way, you ru-ler King, We're bound for South Aus-tra-lia.

Oh, South Aus-tra-lia is my home. Heave a-way, haul a-way. From South Aus-tra-lia

I'll ne'er roam. And we're bound for South Aus-tra-lia. Heave a-way you rul-ler King;

Heave a-way, haul a-way. Heave a-way and hear me sing. We're__ bound for South Aus-tra-lia.

Shanty

Solo: Oh, South Australia's my native home.
Chorus: Heave away! Heave away!
Solo: Oh, South Australia's my native home.
Chorus: We're bound for South Australia.
         Heave away, heave away,
         Oh, heave away, you ruler King,
         We're bound for South Australia.

Solo: There ain't but the one thing grieves my mind.
Chorus: Heave away! Heave away!
Solo: To leave my dear wife and child behind.
Chorus: We're bound for South Australia.
         Heave away, heave away,
         Oh, heave away, you ruler King,
         We're bound for South Australia.

Solo: I see my wife standing on the quay,
Chorus: Heave away! Heave away!
Solo: The tears do start as she waves to me.
Chorus: We're bound for South Australia.
         Heave away, heave away,
         Oh, heave away, you ruler King,
         We're bound for South Australia.

Solo: I'll tell you the truth and I'll tell you no lie;
Chorus: Heave away! Heave away!
Solo: If don't love that girl hope I may die.
Chorus: We're bound for South Australia.
         Heave away, heave away,
         Oh, heave away, you ruler King,
         We're bound for South Australia.

8
Click Go The Shears

Traditional

Out on the board the old shear-er stands,__ Grasp-ing his shears in his thin bo-ny hands;

Fixed is his gaze on a bare - bel - lied yoe, Glo - ry if he gets her, won't he make the ring-er go.__

Chorus

Click go the shears boys, click, click, click,__ Wide is his blow and his hands move quick,__ The

ring - er looks a - round and is beat-en by a blow,__ And curs-es the old snag-ger with the bare-bel-lied yoe.

Out on the board the old shearer stands,
Grasping his shears in his thin bony hands;
Fixed is his gaze on a bare - bellied yoe,
Glory if he gets her, won't he make the ringer go.

Chorus:
Click go the shears boys, click, click, click,
Wide is his blow and his hands move quick,
The ringer looks around and is beaten by a blow,
And curses the old snagger with the bare - bellied yoe.

In the middle of the floor in his cane bottomed chair
Sits the boss of the board with his eyes everywhere,
Notes well each fleece as it comes to the screen,
Paying strict attention that it's taken off clean.

The colonial experience man, he is there of course,
With his shiny leggin's on, just got off his horse,
Gazes all around him like a real connoisseur,
Scented soap, and brilliantine and smelling like a whore.

The tar - boy is there waiting in demand
With his blackened tar - pot, in his tarry hand,
Spies one old sheep with a cut upon its back,
Hears what he's waiting for it's 'Tar here' Jack!'

Now the shearing is all over, we've all got our cheques,
So roll up your swags and it's off down the track,
The first pub we come to it's there we'll have a spree
And everyone that comes along it's 'Have a drink with me.'

There we leave him standing shouting for all hands,
Whilst all around him every 'shouter' stands,
His eye is on the keg which now is lowering fast,
He works hard, he drinks hard, and goes to Hell at last!

9
Down Under

Colin Hay and Ron Strykert

10
Flash Jack From Gundagai

Traditional

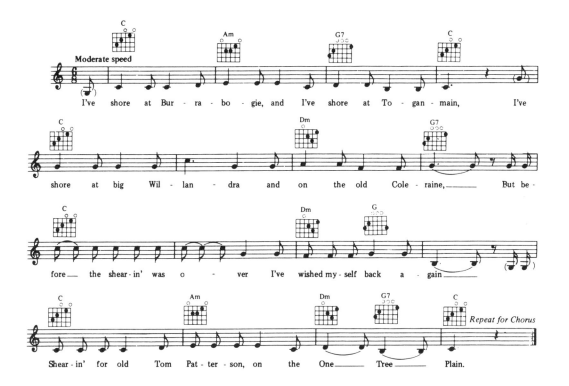

Chorus:
All among the wool, boys, all among the wool,
Keep your blades full boys, keep your blades full.
I can do a respectable tally myself whenever I like to try,
And they know me round the backblocks as Flash Jack from Gundagai.

I've shore at big Willandra and I've shore at Tilberoo,
And once I drew my blades, my boys, upon the famed Barcoo,
At Cowan Downs and Trida, as far as Moulamein,
But I always was glad to get back again to the One Tree Plain.

I've pinked 'em with the Wolseleys and I've rushed with B- bows, too,
And shaved 'em in the grease, my boys, with the grass seed showing through.
But I never slummed my pen, my lads, whate'er it might contain,
While shearin' for old Tom Patterson, on the One Tree Plain.

I've been whalin' up the Lachlan, and I've dossed on Cooper's Creek,
And once I rung Cudjingie shed, and blued it in a week.
But when Gabriel blows his trumpet, lads, I'll catch the morning train,
And I'll push for old Tom Patterson's on the One Tree Plain.

11
From Little Things Big Things Grow

Paul Kelly and Kev Carmody

Gurindji were working for nothing but rations
Where once they had gathered the wealth of the land
Daily the pressure got tighter and tighter
Gurindji decided they must make a stand.
They picked up their swags and started off walking
At Wattie Creek they sat themselves down
Now it don't sound like much but it sure got tongues talking
Back at the homestead and then in the town.

Vestey man said I'll double your wages
Seven quid a week you'll have in your hand
Vincent said "uhuh, we're not talking about wages
We're sitting right here 'till we get our land"
Vestey man roared and Vestey man thundered
"You don't stand the chance of a cinder in snow"
Vince said "if we fall others are rising"

Then Vincent Lingiarri boarded an aeroplane
Landed in Sydney, big city of lights
And daily, he went round softly speaking his story
To all kinds of men from all walks of life.
And Vincent sat down with big politicians
"This affair," they told him, "is a matter of state
Let us sort it out, your people are hungry"
Vincent said "no thanks, we know how to wait"

Then Vincent Lingiarri returned in an aeroplane
Back to his country once more to sit down
And he told his people "let the stars keep on turning
We have friends in the south, cities and towns."
Eight years went by, eight long years of waiting
'Till one day a tall stranger appeared in the land
And he came with lawyers and he came with great ceremony
And through Vincent's fingers poured a handful of sand.

12
I Am Australian

Bruce Woodley and Dobe Newton

I came upon the prison ship bound down by iron chains

I cleared the land, endured the lash and waited for the rains.

I'm a settler, I'm a farmer's wife on a dry and barren run

A convict then a free man, I became Australian.

I'm the daughter of a digger who sought the mother lode

The girl became a woman on the long and dusty road

I'm a child of the depression, I saw the good times come

I'm a bushy, I'm a battler, I am Australian. We are one...

I'm a teller of stories, I'm a singer of songs

I am Albert Namatjira, and I paint the ghostly gums

I am Clancy on his horse, I'm Ned Kelly on the run

I'm the one who waltzed Matilda, I am Australian

I'm the hot wind from the desert, I'm the black soil of the plains

I'm the mountains and the valleys, I'm the drought and flooding rains

I am the rock, I am the sky, the rivers when they run

The spirit of this great land, I am Australian. We are one...

13
Great Southern Land

Ivor Davies

14
Home Among The Gumtrees

W. Johnson and B. Brown

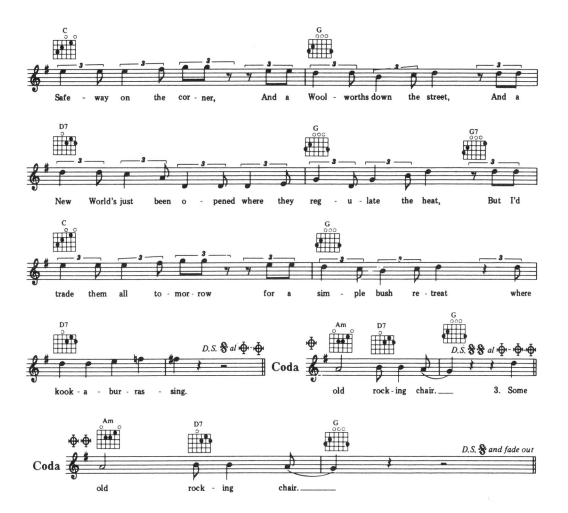

2. I'll be standing in the kitchen
   Cooking up a roast,
   With Vegemite on toast,
   Just me and you, a cockatoo,
   And after tea we'll settle down
   Beside the hitching post,
   And watch the wombats play.

3. Some people like their houses built
   With fences all around,
   Others live in mansions,
   Or in bunkers underground,
   But I won't be content
   Until the day that I have found
   The place I long to be.

15
I Still Call Australia Home

Peter Allen

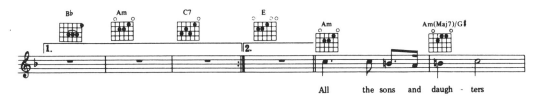

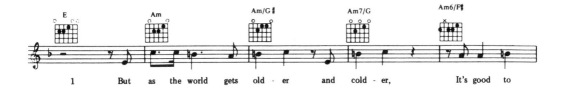

But as the world gets old - er and cold - er, It's good to

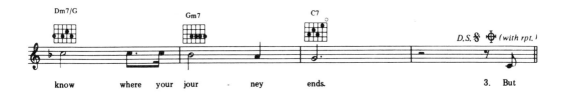

know where your jour - ney ends.

D.S. 𝄋 ⊕ (with rpt.)

3. But

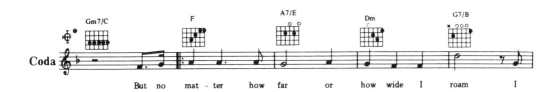

Coda

But no mat - ter how far or how wide I roam I

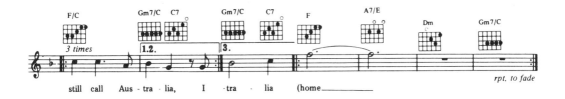

still call Aus - tra - lia, I - tra - lia (home_____

rpt. to fade

Verse 2. I'm always trav'lin', I love being free,
And so I keep leaving the sun and the sea,
But my heart lies waiting over the foam
I still call Australia home.

Verse 3. But someday we'll all be together once more
When all of the ships came back to the shore,
I realize something I've always known
I still call Australia home.

16
Kookaburra Sits In The Old Gum Tree

Marion Sinclair

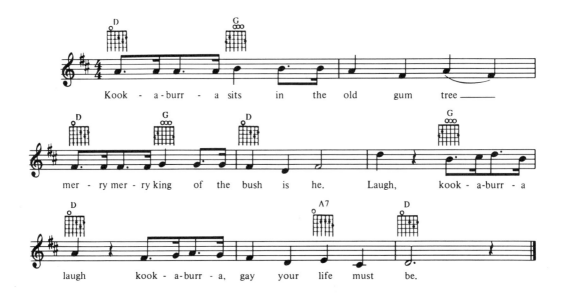

Kook - a - burr - a sits in the old gum tree _____ mer - ry mer - ry king of the bush is he. Laugh, kook - a - burr - a laugh kook - a - burr - a, gay your life must be.

17
Lachlan Tigers (The)

Traditional

1. Now at his gate each shear-er stood as the whis-tle loud-ly blew. With
eye-brows fixed and lips com-pressed the ti-gers all bent too; You could
hear the click-ing of the shears as through the wool they glide. You
see a gun al-read-y turned he's on the whip-ping side (V2. At)

At his gate each shearer stood as the whistle loudly blew,
With eyebrows fixed and lips compressed the tigers all bent too;
You could hear the clicking of the shears as through the wool they glide,
You see a gun already turned, he's on the whipping side.

Chorus:
A lot of Lachlan tigers it's plain to see we are,
Hark to our burly ringer as he loudly calls for tar;
'Tar here,' calls one and quick the tar boy flies
'Sweep those locks away,' another loudly cries.

The scene it is a lively one and ought to be admired,
There hasn't been a better board since Jacky Howe expired;
Along the board our gaffer walks his face all in a frown,
And passing by the ringer says, 'You watch my lad, keep down,'

For I must have their bellies off, and topknots too likewise,
My eye is quick so none of your tricks or from me you will fly,
Oh, curses on our gaffer, he's never on our side,
To shear a decent tally boys, in vain I've often tried.

I have a pair of Ward and Paine's that are both bright and new,
I'll rig them up and I'll let you see what I can really do!
For I've shorn on the Riverine where they shear 'em by the score
But such a terror as this to clip I never shore before.

18
Ladies Of Brisbane

Traditional

Fare - well and a - dieu to you, sweet Bris - bane la - dies, Fare - well and a -

dieu to you girls of Too - wong, For we've sold all our cat - tle, and

Repeat for Chorus

have to be mo - ving, But we hope we shall see you a - gain be - fore long.

Chorus:
We'll rant and we'll roar like true Queensland drovers,
We'll rant and we'll roar as onwards we push,
Until we get back to the Augathella Station,
For it's flaming dry going through the old Queensland bush.

The first camp we make, we shall call it the Quart - pot,
Caboolture, then Kilcoy and Colinton's Hut;
We'll pull up at the Stone House, Bob Williamson's paddock,
And early next morning we cross the Blackbutt.

Then on to Taromeo and Yarraman Creek, lads,
It's there we shall make our next camp for the day,
Where the water and grass are both plenty and sweet, lads,
And maybe we'll butcher a fat little stray.

Then on to Nanango, that hardbitten township,
Where the out - of - work station hands sit in the dust,
And the shearers get shorn by old Tim the contractor -
Oh I wouldn't go near there but I flaming well must!

The girls of Toomancey, they look so entrancing,
Those young bawling heifers are out for their fun!
With the waltz and the polka and all kinds of dancing,
To the racketty old banjo of Bob Anderson.

Then fill up your glasses and drink to the lasses;
We'll drink this town dry, then farewell to them all;
And when we've got back to the Augathella Station
We'll hope you come by there and pay us a call.

19
Lime Juice Tub

Traditional

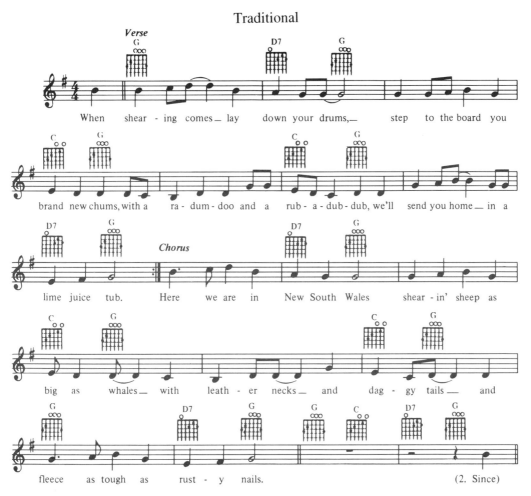

When shear-ing comes— lay down your drums,— step to the board you brand new chums, with a ra - dum - doo and a rub - a - dub - dub, we'll send you home— in a lime juice tub.

Chorus

Here we are in New South Wales shear-in' sheep as big as whales— with leath - er necks— and dag - gy tails — and fleece as tough as rust - y nails.

(2. Since)

V1. When shearing comes lay down your drums,
Step to the board, you brand new chums,
With a ra-dum-doo and a rub-a-dub-dub
We'll send you home in a lime-juice tub.

V2. Since you have crossed the briny deep
You fancy you can shear a sheep,
With a ra-dum-doo and a rub-a-dub-dub
We'll send you home in a lime-juice tub.

Chrous:
V3. Here we are in New South Wales
Shearing sheep as big as whales
With leather necks and daggy tails
and fleece as tough as rusty nails.

V4. There's cockies' sons and brand new chums
Who fancy that they're all great guns.
They fancy they can shear the wool
The buggers can only tear and pull.

They tar the sheep till they're nearly black
Roll up, roll up, and get the sack
Once more we're away on the wallaby track
More to look for work out back.

V5. And when they're out upon the road
From off their backs they throw their load
And at the sun they take a look
And reckon that it's time to press the cook.

V6. They sleep in huts without any door
And camp upon the dirty floor,
With a pannikin of flour and a sheet of bark
To wallop up a damper in the dark.

V7. You cockies, too, you never need fret
For I'm the man who's willing to bet
You're up to your eyes, heels first in debt
You're up to your eyes, your sons as well.

V8. Although you live beyond your means,
Your daughters wear no crinolines
Nor are they covered by boots and shoes
They're wild in the bush with the kangaroos.

V9. It's home, it's home I'd like to be,
Not humpin' me drum in this sheep country
Over a thousand miles I've come
To march along with a blanket drum.

V10. But shearing's here, boys, give a cheer
Step to the board and grab your gear
With a ra-dum-doo and a rub-a-dub-dub

20
Our Don Bradman

Jack O'Hagan

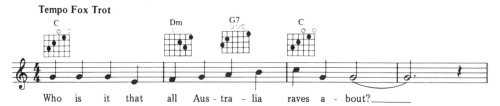

Who is it that all Aus - tra - lia raves a - bout?_____

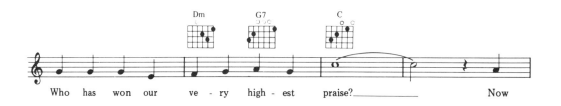

Who has won our ve - ry high - est praise?_____ Now

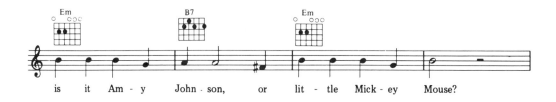

is it Am - y John - son, or lit - tle Mick - ey Mouse?

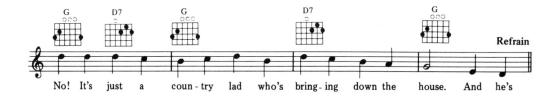

No! It's just a coun - try lad who's bring - ing down the house. And he's

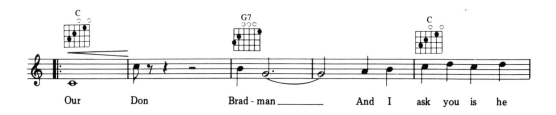

Our Don Brad - man_____ And I ask you is he

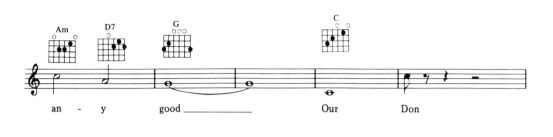

an - y good _____ Our Don

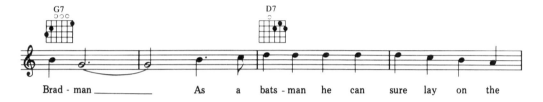

Brad - man _____ As a bats - man he can sure lay on the

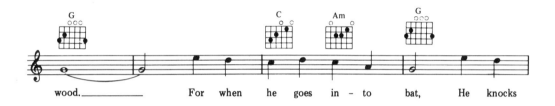

wood. _____ For when he goes in - to bat, He knocks

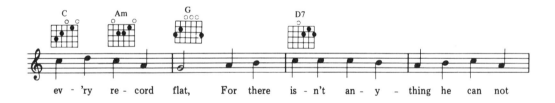

ev - 'ry re - cord flat, For there is - n't an - y - thing he can not

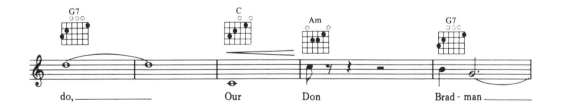

do, _____ Our Don Brad - man _____

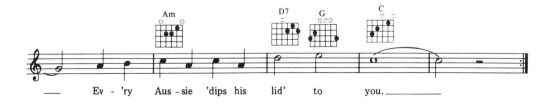

_____ Ev - 'ry Aus - sie 'dips his lid' to you. _____

21
Overlander (The)

Traditional

1.There's a trade you all know well it's_ bring-ing cat-tle o-ver on_

ev - 'ry track to the gulf and back men know the Queens-land dro-ver so_

pass the bil-ly 'round, boys don't let the pint pot stand there for to -

night well drink the health of ev - ry Ov - er - land - er.

V2. I come from Northern plains
Where the girls and grass are scanty
Where the creeks run dry or ten feet high
And it's either drought or plenty.

V3. There are men from ev'ry land
From, Spain and France and Flanders
They're a well mixed pack, both white and black
The Queensland Overlanders

V4. When wev'e earned a spree in town
We live like pigs in clover
And the whole damn cheque pours down the neck
Of many a Queensland drover

V5. As I pass along the road,
The children raise my dander
Shouting "Mother dear, take in the clothes
Here comes an overlander"

V6. There's a girl in Sydney Town
Who said "Please don't leave me lonely"
I said "It's sad,
But my old Prad has room for one man only

V7. But I'm bound for home once more
On a Prad that's quite a goer
I can find a job with a crawling mob
On the banks of the Maranoa

22
Queensland Drover (The)

Traditional

There's a trade you all know well,
It's bringing cattle over.
On every track, to the Gulf and back,
Men know the Queensland drover.

Chorus:
Pass the billy round, my boys!
Don't let the pint-pot stand there!
For tonight we drink the health
Of every overlander.

I come from the Northern plains
Where the girls and grass are scanty;
Where the creeks run dry or ten foot high
And it's either drought or plenty.

There are men from every land,
From Spain and France and Flanders;
They're a well-mixed pack, both white and black,
The Queensland overlanders.

When we've earned a spree in town
We live like pigs in clover;
And the whole year's cheque pours down the neck
Of many a Queensland drover.

As I pass along the roads,
The children raise my dander
Crying 'Mother dear, take in the clothes,
Here comes an overlander!'

Now I'm bound for home once more,
On a prad that's quite a goer;
I can find a job with a crawling mob
On the banks of the Maranoa.

23
Ryebuck Shearer

Traditional

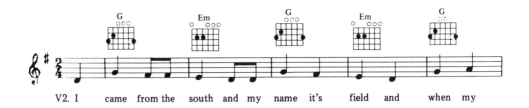

V2. I came from the south and my name it's field and when my

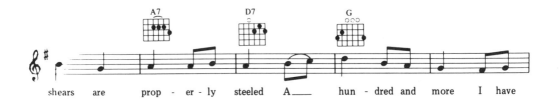

shears are prop - er - ly steeled A____ hun - dred and more I have

ve - ry of - ten peeled and of course I'm a rye - buck____ shear - er.

CHORUS: If I don't shear a tally before I go
My shears and stone in the river I'll throw
I'll never open sawbees to take another blow
And prove I'm a ryebuck shearer.

V2. There's a bloke on the board and he's got a yellow skin
A very long nose and he shaves on the chin
And a voice like a billy - goat dancing on a tin
And of course he's a ryebuck shearer

V3. There's a bloke on the board and I heard him say
That I couldn't sheer a hundred sheep in a day
But some fine day I'll show him the way
And prove I'm a ryebuck shearer

V4. Oh I'll make a splash but I won't say when
I'll hop off me tail and I'll into the pen
While the ringers shearing five I'll shear ten
And prove I'm a ryebuck shearer

24
Tie Me Kangaroo Down Sport

Rolf Harris

Recitation over F chord

There's an old Australian stockman, lying, dying, And he gets himself up on one elbow, And he turns to his mates, who are gathered 'round him and he says:

1. Watch me wal - la - bys feed, mate, Watch me wal - la - bys feed.

They're a dan - ger - ous breed, mate, So watch me wal - la - bys feed. Al - to - geth - er now!

Tie me kan - ga - roo down sport, Tie me kan - ga - roo down.

Tie me kan - ga - roo down, sport, Tie me kan - ga - roo down. Al - to - geth - er now! down.

2. Keep me cockatoo cool, Curl,
Keep me cockatoo cool.
Don't go acting the fool, Curl,
Just keep me cockatoo cool. .
Altogether now!

3. Take me koala back, Jack,
Take me koala back.
He lives some where out on the track, Mac,
So take me koala back.
Altogether now!

4. Let me abos go loose, Lew,
Let me abos go loose.
They're of no further use, Lew,
So let me abos go loose.
Altogether now!

5. Mind me platypus duck, Bill,
Mind me platypus duck.
Don't let him go running amok, Bill,
Mind me platypus duck.
Altogether now!

6. Play your didgeridoo, Blue,
Play your didgeridoo.
Keep playing 'til I shoot thro' Blue,
Play your didgeridoo.
Altogether now!

7. Tan me hide when I'm dead, Fred,
Tan me hide when I'm dead.
So we tanned his hide when he died Clyde,
(Spoken) And that's it hanging on the shed.
Altogether now!

25
Shores Of Botany Bay

Traditional

I'm on me way down to the quay where the big ship now doth lay. To com-
mand a gang of nav-vies I was or-dered to en-gage. And I
thought I would stop in for a while be-fore I sailed a-way to ____
take a trip on an im-mi-grant ship to the shores of Bot-n'y Bay. Fare-

Chorus

well to your bricks and mor-tar, Fare-well to your dirt-y lime. Farewell to your gang-way and your gang plank, and to hell with your o-ver-
time. For the good ship Rag-a-muf-fin she's

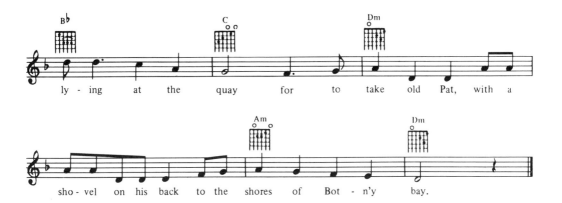

ly - ing at the quay for to take old Pat, with a

sho - vel on his back to the shores of Bot - n'y bay.

2. The best years of our lives we spend
   At working on the docks
   Building mighty wharves and quays
   Of earth and ballast rocks
   Our pensions keep our lives secure,
   But I'll not rue the day
   When I take a trip, on an immigrant ship,
   To the shores of Botany Bay.

3. The boss came out this morning
   And he said 'Why Pat, hello,
   If you do not mix the mortar quick
   Be sure you'll have to go.'
   Well of course he did insult me
   And I demanded all me pay,
   And I told him straight I was going to emigrate
   To the shores of Botany Bay.

4. And when I reach Australia
   I'll go and search for gold
   There's plenty there for digging up
   Or so I have been told.
   Or maybe I'll go back to me trade,
   Eight hundred bricks I'll lay
   For an eight-hour shift and an eight bob pay
   On the shores of Botany Bay.

26
True Blue

John Williamson

27
Waltzing Matilda

A.B. Patterson and Marie Cowan

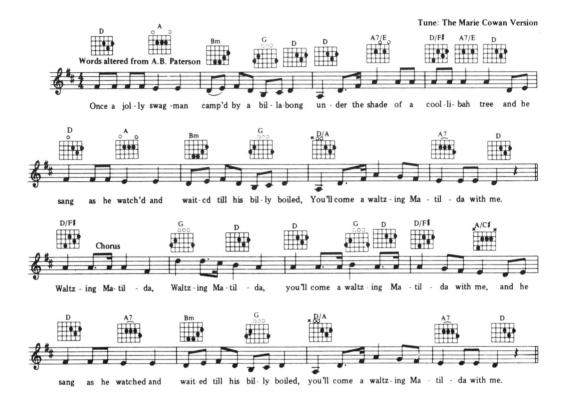

Tune: The Marie Cowan Version

Words altered from A.B. Paterson

Once a jol-ly swag-man camp'd by a bil-la-bong un-der the shade of a cool-li-bah tree and he

sang as he watch'd and wait-ed till his bil-ly boiled, You'll come a waltz-ing Ma-til-da with me.

Chorus

Waltz-ing Ma-til-da, Waltz-ing Ma-til-da, you'll come a waltz-ing Ma-til-da with me, and he

sang as he watched and wait-ed till his bil-ly boiled, you'll come a waltz-ing Ma-til-da with me.

1. Oh, there once was a swagman camped in a billabong,
   Under the shade of a coolibah tree;
   And he sang as he looked at his old billy boiling,
   'Who'll come a - waltzing Matilda with me?'

   Chorus: Who'll come a - waltzing Matilda, my darling?
   Who'll come a - waltzing Matilda with me?
   Waltzing Matilda and leading a water - bag -
   Who'll come a - waltzing Matilda with me?

2. Down came a jumbuck to drink at the water - hole,
   Up jumped the swagman and grabbed him with glee;
   And he sang as he stowed him away in his tucker - bag,
   'You'll come a - waltzing Matilda with me.'

3. Down came the Squatter a - riding his thoroughbred;
   Down came Policemen - one, two and three.
   'Whose is the jumbuck you've got in the tucker - bag?
   You'll come a - waltzing Matilda with me.'

4. But the swagman he up and he jumped in the water - hole,
   Drowning himself by the coolibah tree;
   And his ghost may be heard as it sings in the billabong
   'Who'll come a - waltzing Matilda with me?'

28
Where The Dog Sits On The Tuckerbox

Jack O'Hagan

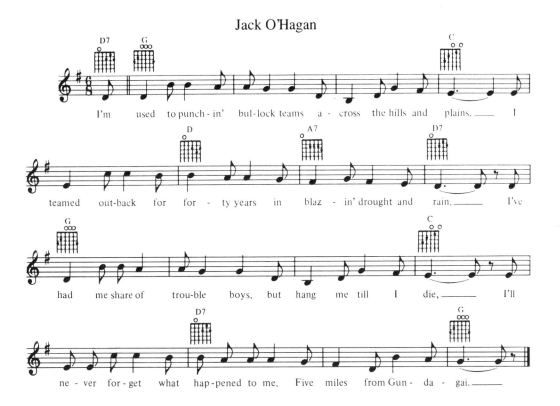

I'm used to punch-in' bul-lock teams a-cross the hills and plains,___ I teamed out-back for for-ty years in blaz-in' drought and rain,___ I've had me share of trou-ble boys, but hang me till I die,___ I'll ne-ver for-get what hap-pened to me. Five miles from Gun-da-gai.___

2. It was raining hard, the team got bogged,
   The axle snapped in two,
   I'd lost me matches and me pipe,
   Lord, what was I to do?
   The rain came down, 'twas bitter cold,
   And hungry too was I,
   And the dog sat in the tucker box,
   Five miles from Gundagai.

3. Some blokes I know have lots of luck,
   No matter where they fall.
   But there was I, Lord love-a-duck!
   No flamin' luck at all.
   I couldn't make a pot of tea
   Or keep me trousers dry,
   And the dog,
   Sat in the tucker box,
   Five miles from Gundagai.

4. I can forgive the dark and cold,
   I can forgive the rain.
   I can forgive me flamin' team;
   And go through it again.
   I can forgive me rotten luck,
   But hang me till I die,
   I can't forgive that bloody dog,
   Five miles from Gundagai.

29
Wild Colonial Boy (The)

Traditional

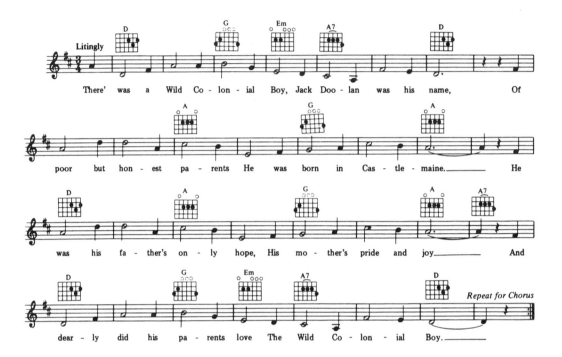

1. There was a Wild Colonial Boy,
   Jack Doolan was his name,
   Of poor but honest parents
   He was born in Castlemaine.
   He was his father's only hope,
   His mother's pride and joy
   And dearly did his parents love
   The Wild Colonial Boy.

   Chorus:
   So come away me hearties
   We'll roam the mountains high,
   Together we will plunder
   And together we will die.
   We'll scour along the valleys
   And we'll gallop o'er the plains,
   And scorn to live in slavery,
   Bound down by iron chains.

2. At the age of sixteen years
   He left his native home,
   And to Australia's sunny shores,
   A bushranger did roam.
   They put him in the iron gang
   In the government employ,
   But never an iron on earth could hold
   The Wild Colonial Boy.

3. In sixty - one this daring youth
   Commenced his wild career,
   With a heart that knew no danger
   And no foeman did he fear.
   He stuck up the Beechworth mail coach
   And robbed Judge MacEvoy
   Who, trembling cold, gave up his gold
   To the Wild Colonial Boy.

4. He bade the Judge good morning
   And he told him to beware,
   That he'd never rob a needy man
   Or one who acted square,
   But a Judge who'd rob a mother
   Of her one and only joy
   Sure, he must be a worse outlaw than
   The Wild Colonial Boy.

5. One day as Jack was riding
   The mountainside along,
   A- listening to the little birds,
   Their happy laughing song.
   Three mounted troopers came along,
   Kelly, Davis and Fitzroy
   With a warrant for the capture of
   The Wild Colonial Boy.

6. 'Surrender now! Jack Doolan,
   For you see it's three to one;
   Surrender in the Queen's own name,
   You are a highwayman.'
   Jack drew a pistol from his belt
   And waved it like a toy,
   'I'll fight, but not surrender,' cried
   The Wild Colonial Boy.

7. He fired at trooper Kelly
   And brought him to the ground,
   And in return from Davis
   Received a mortal wound,
   All shattered through the jaws he lay
   Still firing, at Fitzroy.
   And that's the way they captured him,
   The Wild Colonial Boy.

30
With My Swag All On My Shoulder

Traditional

When first I left old Ireland's shore, the yarns that we were told Of
how the folks in far Australia could pick up lumps of gold! How
With my

gold - dust lay in all the streets and mi - ner's right was free! 'Hur-
swag all on my shoul - der, black bil - ly in my hand, I'll

rah!' I told my lov - ing friends, 'That's just the place for me!'
travel the bush of Aus - tra - li - a like a true - born I - rish - man.

We made our way into Geelong, then north to Ballarat,
Where some of us grew mighty thin, and some grew sleek and fat.
Some tried their luck at Bendigo and some at Fiery Creek;
I made my fortune in a day and blued it in a week!

Chorus:
With my swag all on my shoulder, black billy in my hand,
I travelled the bush of Australia like a trueborn Irishman.

For many years I wandered round to each new field about,
And made and spent full many a pound till alluvial petered out.
And then for any job of work I was prepared to try,
But now I've found the tucker track, I'll stay there till I die.

Chorus:
With my swag all on my shoulder, black billy in my hand,
I'll travel the bush of Australia like a trueborn Irishman.